The MOOMIN Colouring Book

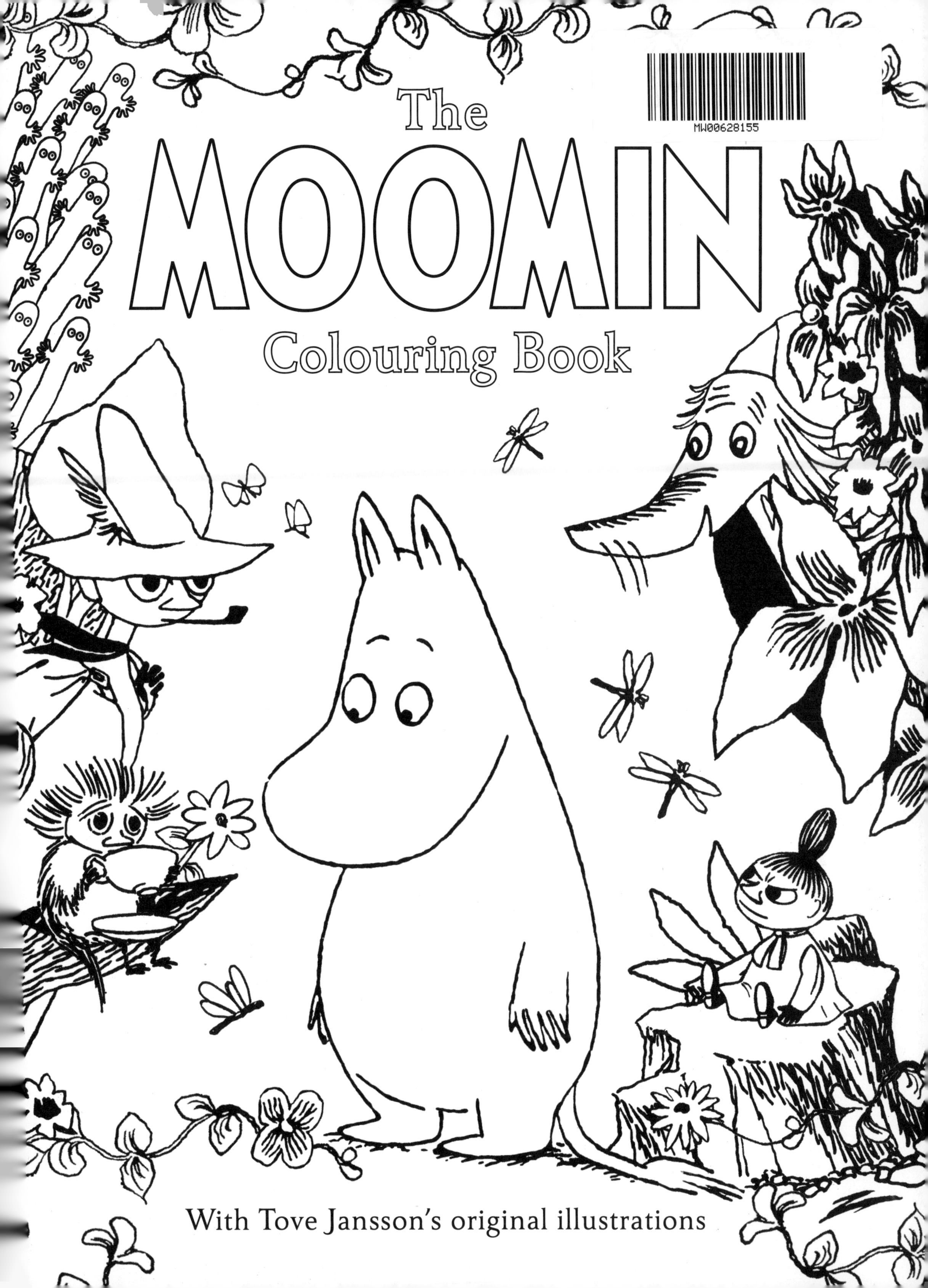

With Tove Jansson's original illustrations

Moomintroll was lying in his customary place (or one of his places) curled up on the green-and-yellow moss with his tail carefully tucked in under him.

- Moominsummer Madness

It is strange how deftly people like the Mys get on in life.

- Moominland Midwinter

'Anyway, if you're
not afraid, I'm
not either!'
Snorkmaiden
- Comet in Moominland

'We went off
to pick nine
kinds of
flowers and
put them under
our pillow and
then our dreams
came true.'
Snorkmaiden
- *Moominsummer Madness*

Tove

She didn’t
awake at first
even when a
fishing-hook
came flying and
caught in the
work-basket.

- Moominsummer Madness

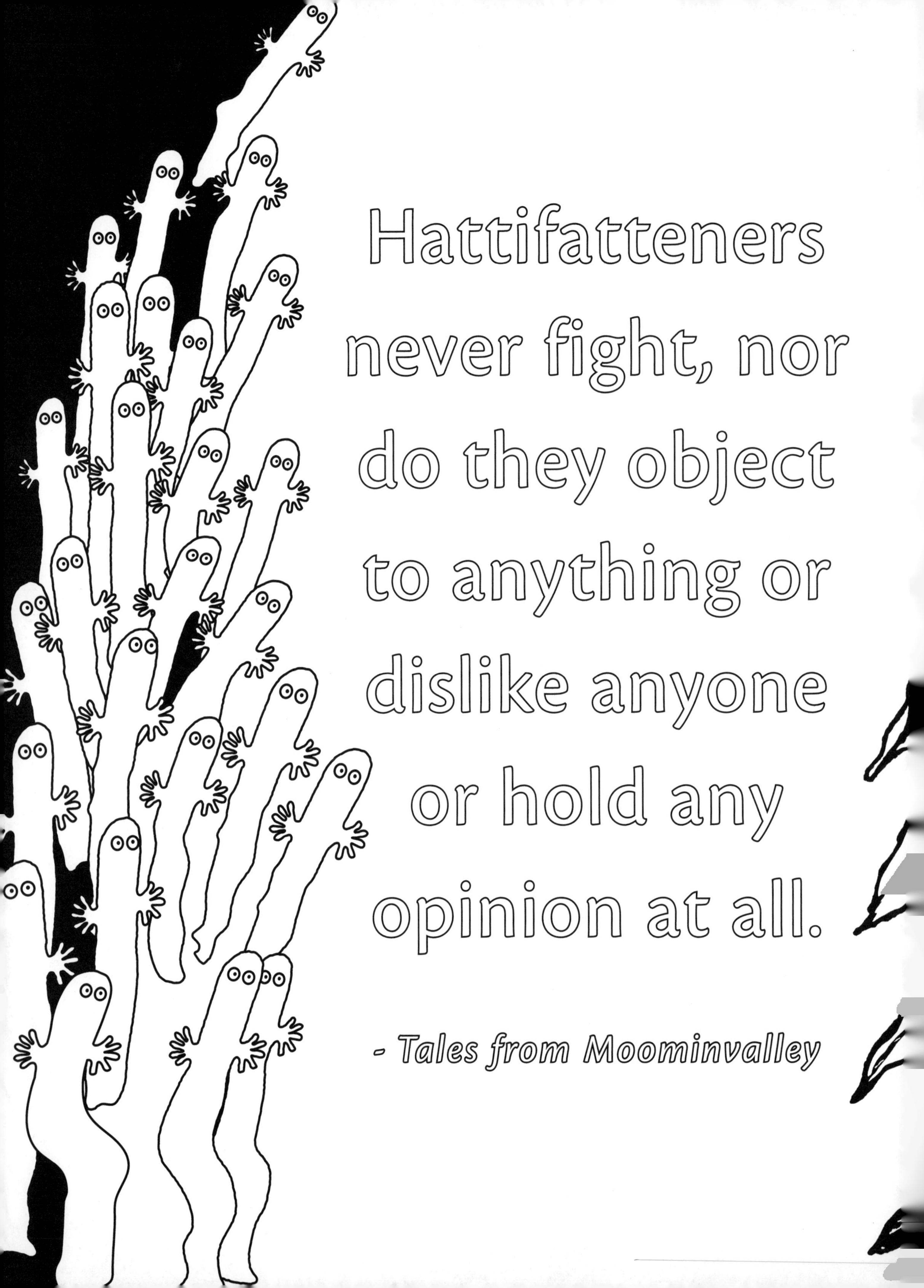
Hattifatteners
never fight, nor
do they object
to anything or
dislike anyone
or hold any
opinion at all.
- Tales from Moominvalley

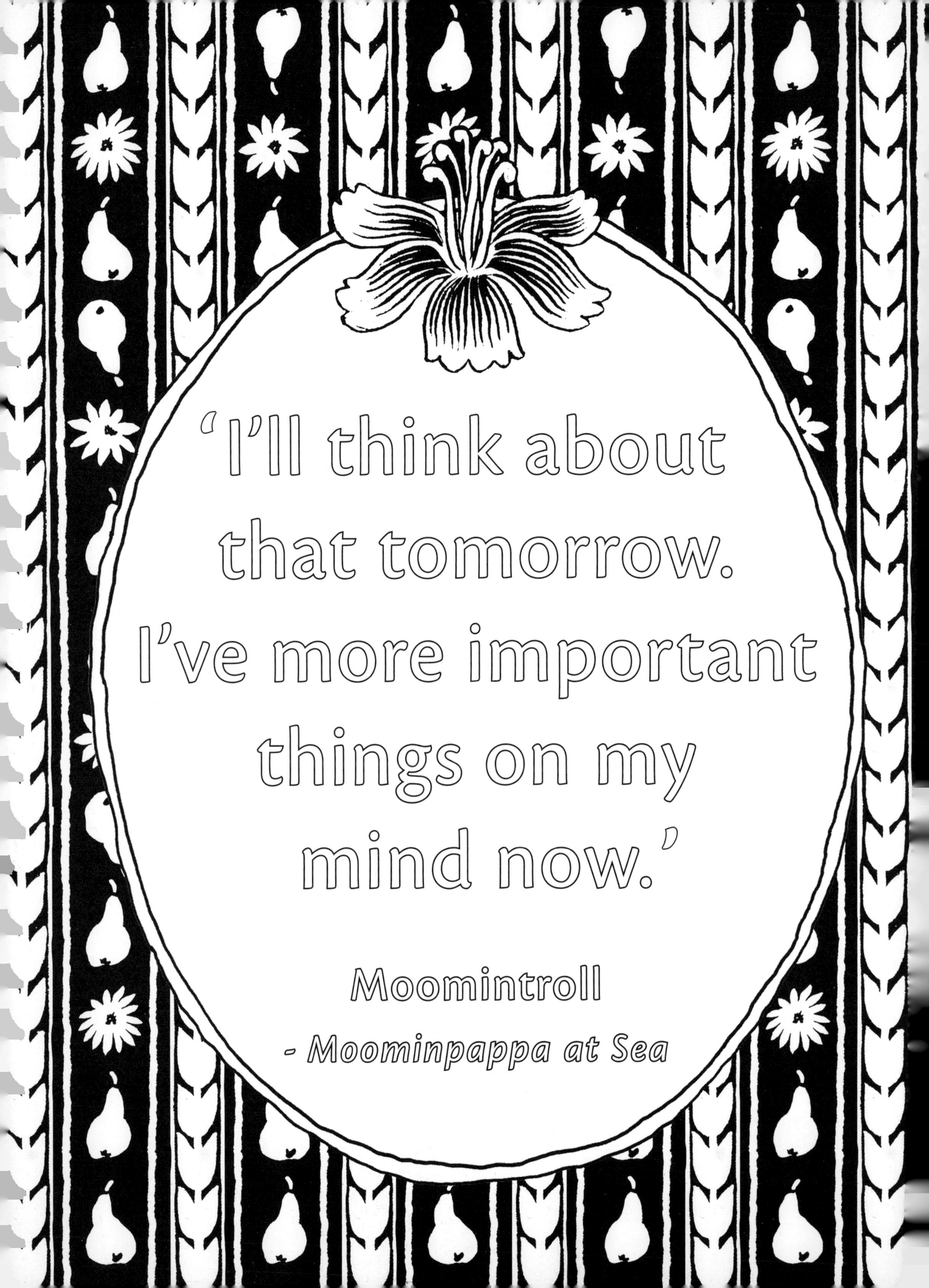
'I'll think about
that tomorrow.
I've more important
things on my
mind now.'
Moomintroll
- Moominpappa at Sea

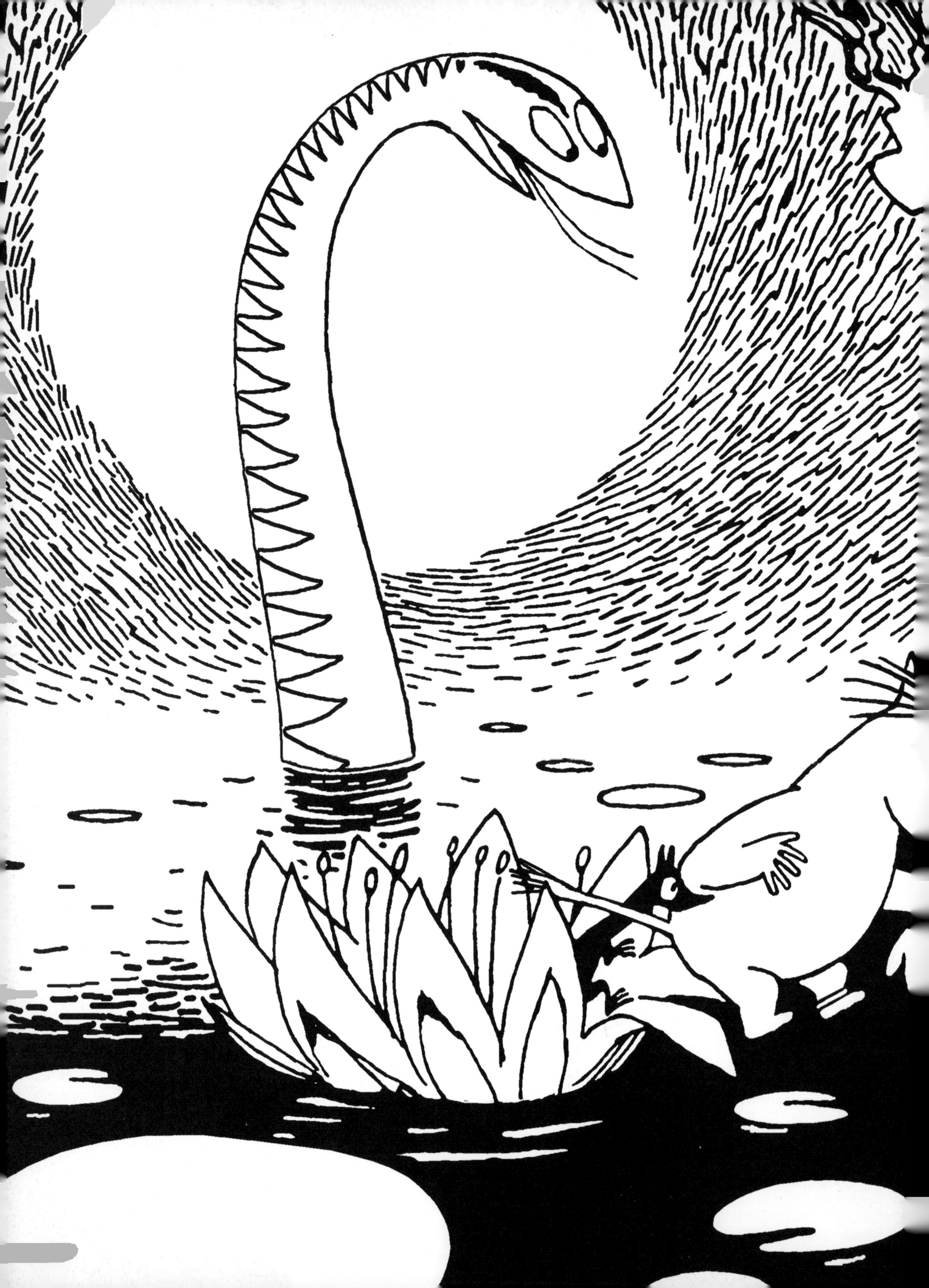

For if you're not afraid how can you be really brave?
- The Exploits of Moominpappa

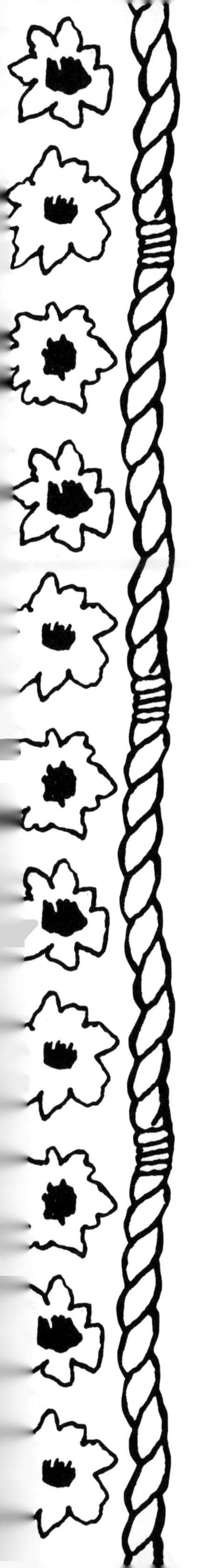

‘There’s no need to worry or fear or fret: There’s plenty of life in all of us yet.’

Snufkin

- Finn Family Moomintroll

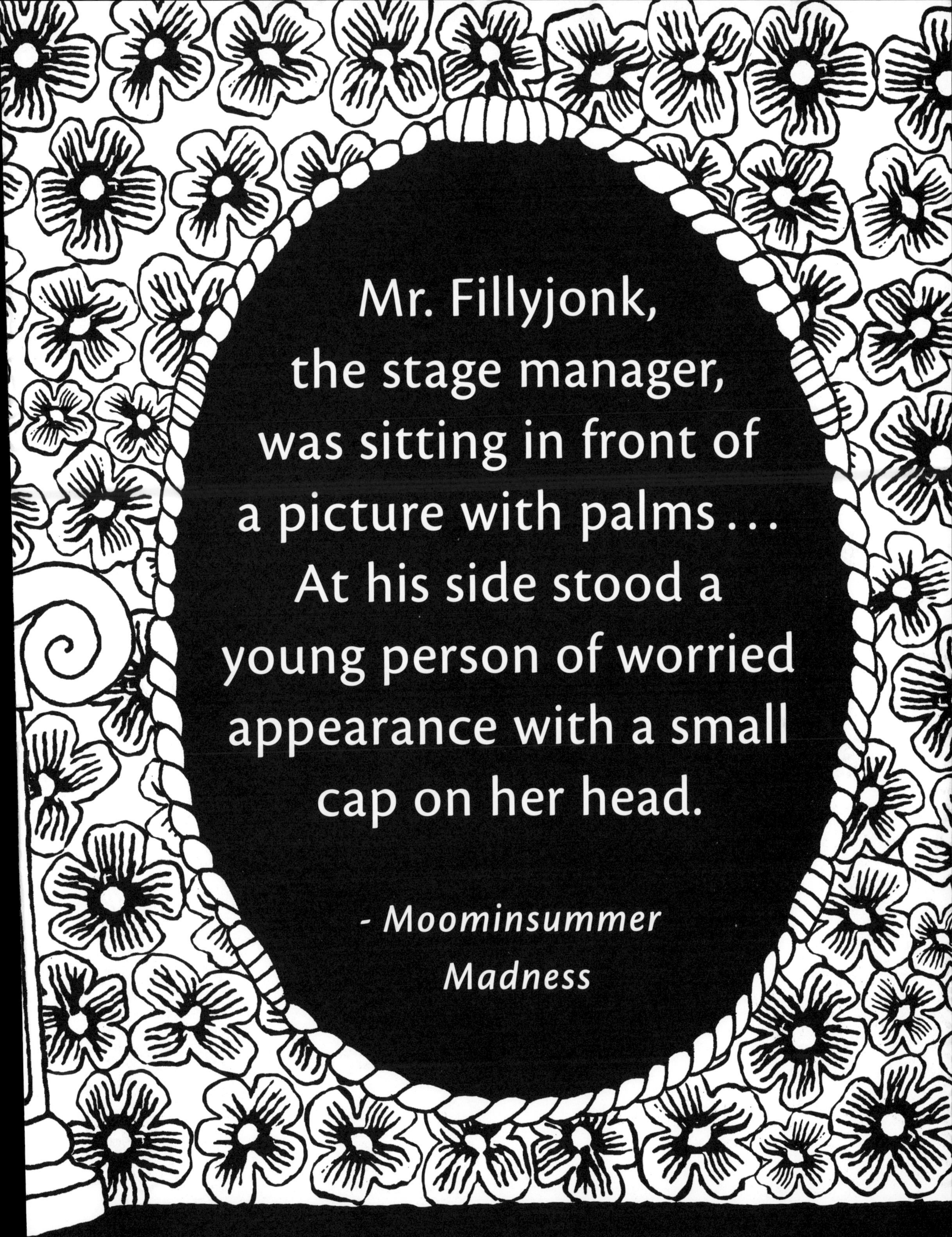
Mr. Fillyjonk,
the stage manager,
was sitting in front of
a picture with palms . . .
At his side stood a
young person of worried
appearance with a small
cap on her head.
- Moominsummer
Madness

‘Such a lot of work may turn out to be really harmful . . . I had a cousin once who studied trigonometry until his whiskers drooped, and when he had learnt it all a Groke came and ate him up.’

The Joxter

- The Exploits of Moominpappa

'One needs a change sometimes. We take everything too much for granted, including each other.'

Moominmamma

- Moominpappa at Sea

Thingumy and Bob sighed contentedly and settled down to contemplate the precious stone.

- Finn Family Moomintroll

The Groke
remained
immobile for
a moment...
Then she glided
down to the
ice again and
back into the
dark, as she
had come,
alone.
- Moominland
Midwinter

'Oh how wonderful! Oh how beautiful!'

Snorkmaiden

- Moominsummer Madness

A new door to
the Unbelievable,
to the Possible,
a new day that
can always bring
you anything
if you have no
objection to it.

- The Exploits of
Moominpappa

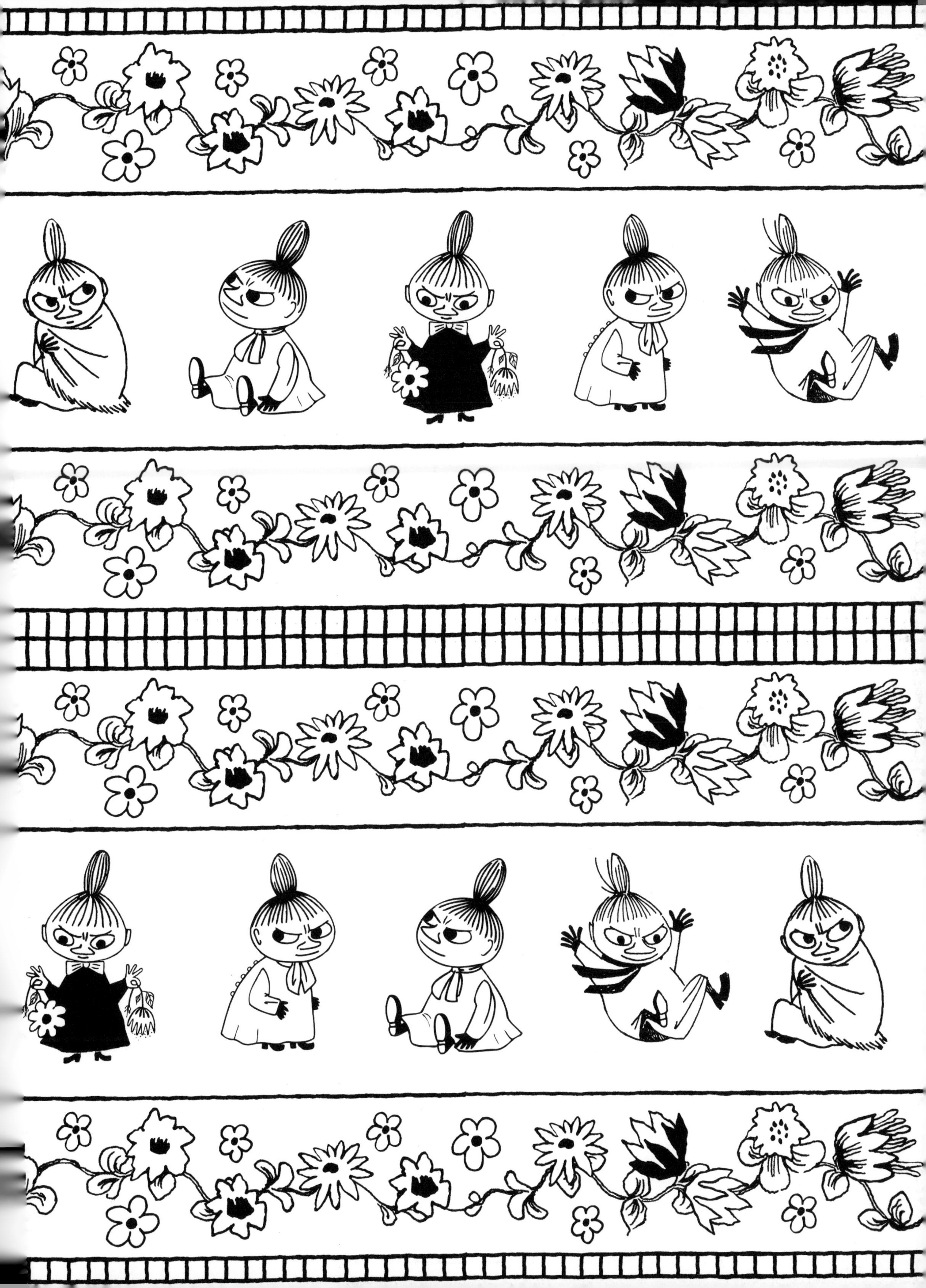

'Well, things can't get much worse – that's one consolation.'
The Muskrat
- Finn Family Moomintroll

He ran
straight out into
the breakers without
stopping to undress
(because of course
Moomintrolls don’t
wear clothes, except
sometimes in bed).
- Comet in
Moominland

'You don't know a thing about the theatre, that's clear, less than nothing, not even the shadow of a thing!'

Emma, the Theatre Rat

- Moominsummer Madness

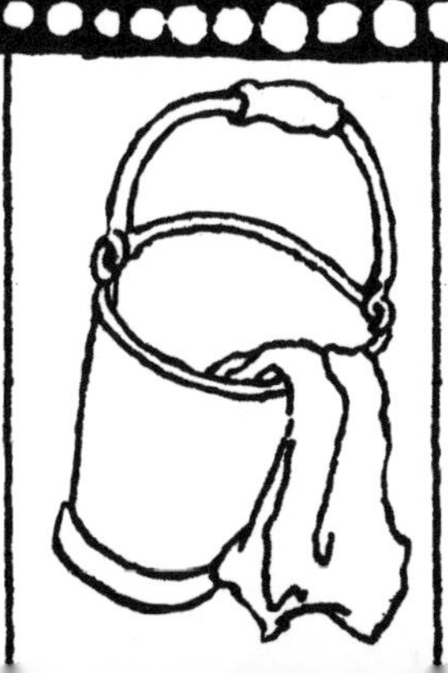

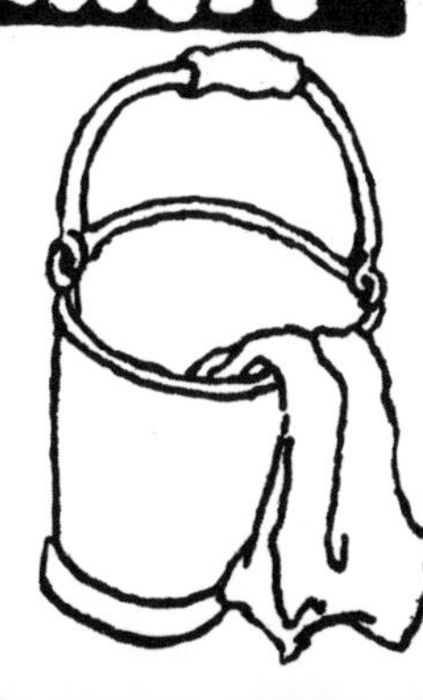

Moominpappa… believed in his hat; it was black and resolute, and inside it Moominmamma had painted the words, 'M.P. from your M.M.' to distinguish it from all other high hats in the world.

- Tales from Moominvalley

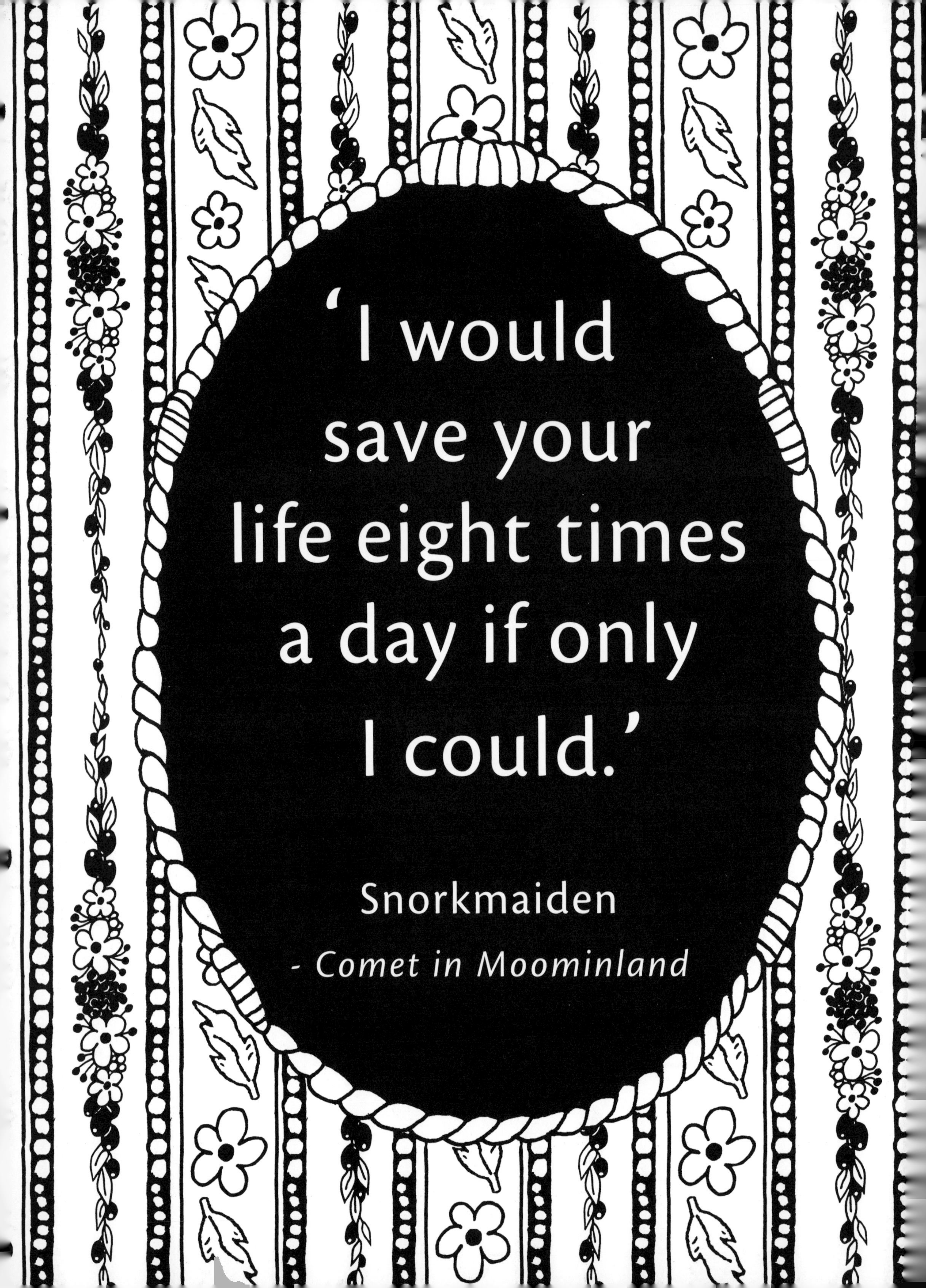
'I would
save your
life eight times
a day if only
I could.'
Snorkmaiden
- Comet in Moominland

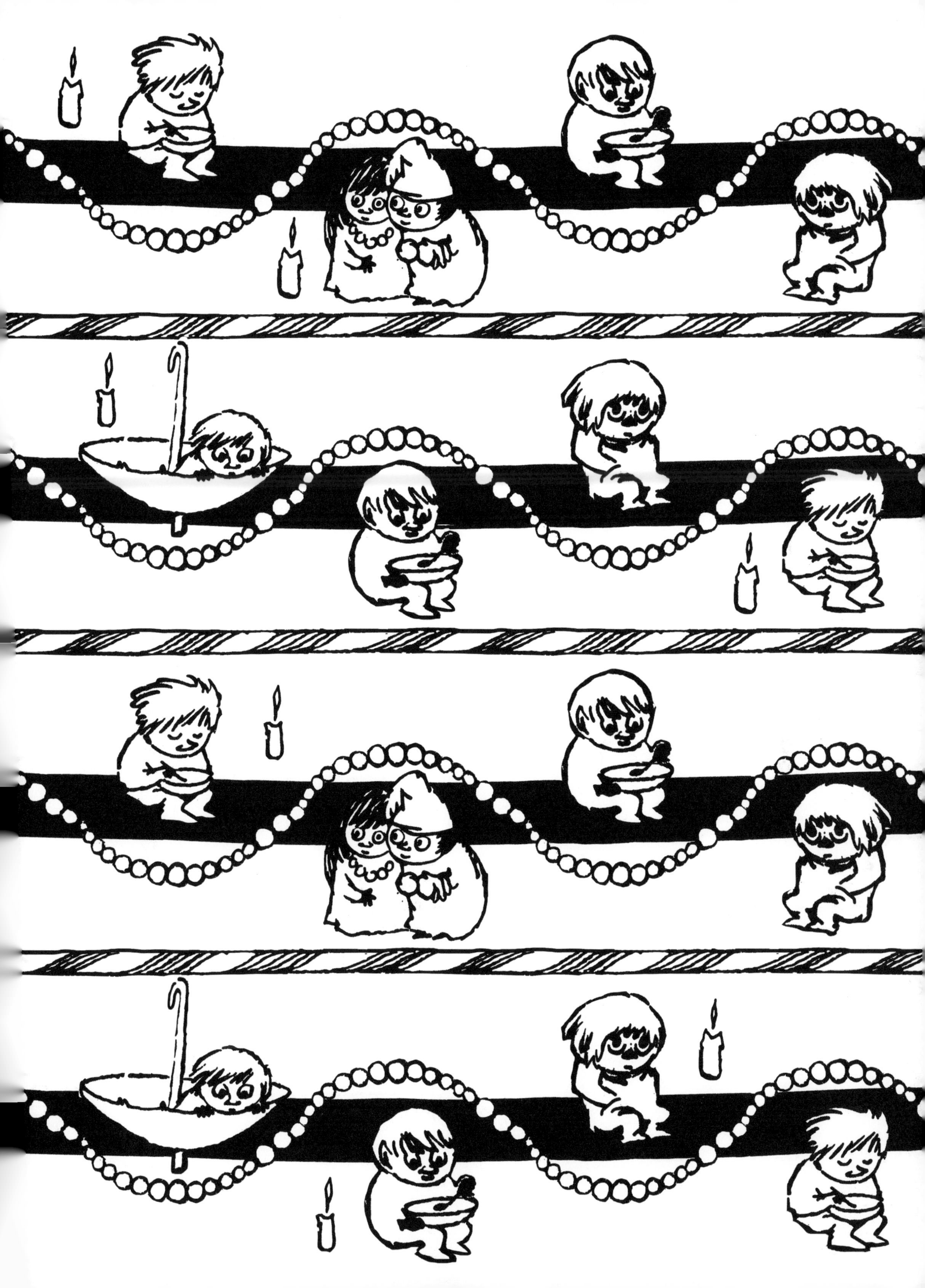

‘ We’re going to keep things in order from now on! ’

The Hemulen Aunt

- *The Exploits of Moominpappa*

First published 2016 by Macmillan Children's Books
an imprint of Pan Macmillan
20 New Wharf Road, London N1 9RR
Associated companies throughout the world
www.panmacmillan.com

ISBN 978-1-5098-1002-4

3 5 7 9 8 6 4

A CIP catalogue record for this book is available from the British Library.

Printed in China

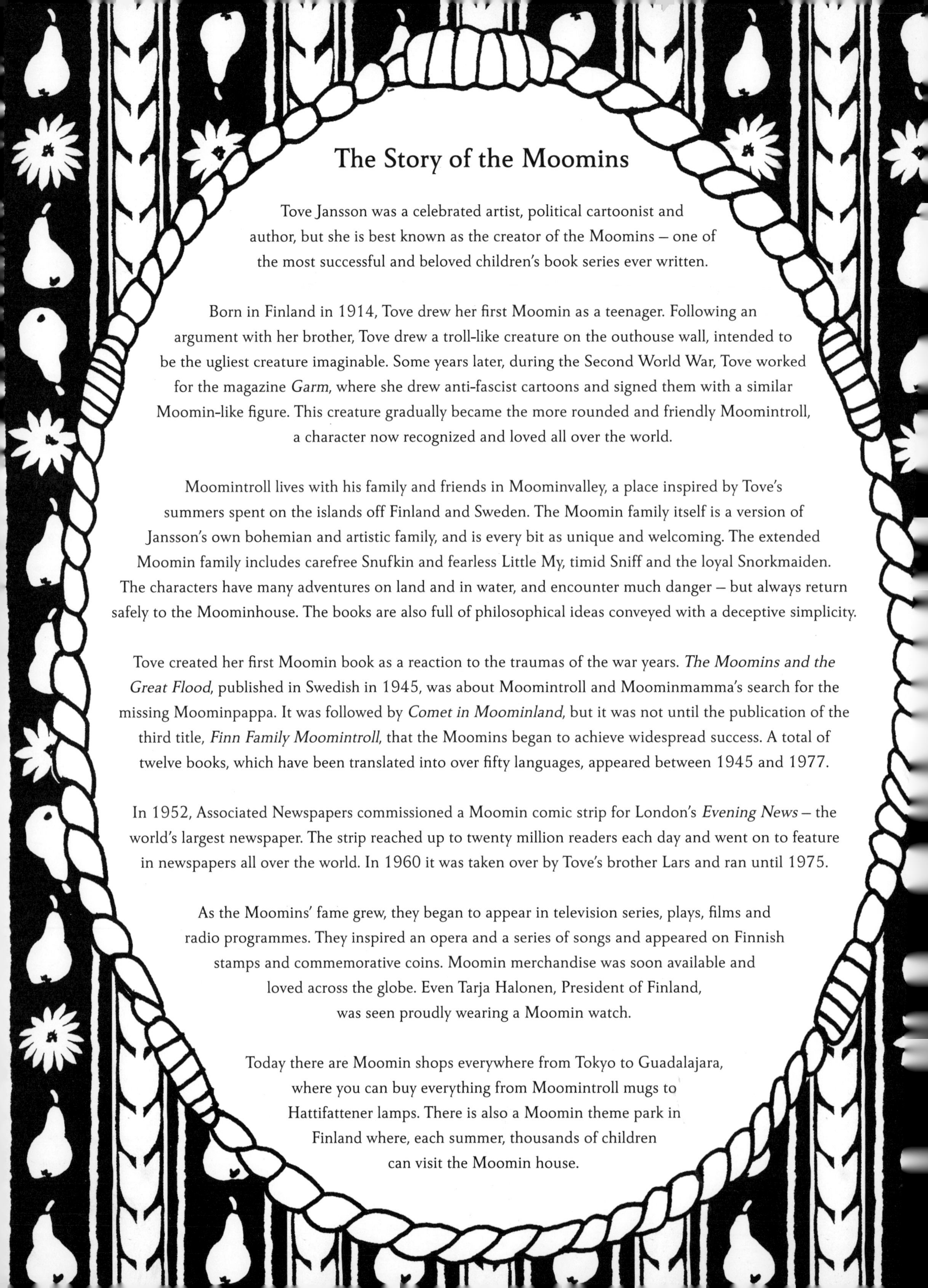

The Story of the Moomins

Tove Jansson was a celebrated artist, political cartoonist and author, but she is best known as the creator of the Moomins – one of the most successful and beloved children's book series ever written.

Born in Finland in 1914, Tove drew her first Moomin as a teenager. Following an argument with her brother, Tove drew a troll-like creature on the outhouse wall, intended to be the ugliest creature imaginable. Some years later, during the Second World War, Tove worked for the magazine *Garm*, where she drew anti-fascist cartoons and signed them with a similar Moomin-like figure. This creature gradually became the more rounded and friendly Moomintroll, a character now recognized and loved all over the world.

Moomintroll lives with his family and friends in Moominvalley, a place inspired by Tove's summers spent on the islands off Finland and Sweden. The Moomin family itself is a version of Jansson's own bohemian and artistic family, and is every bit as unique and welcoming. The extended Moomin family includes carefree Snufkin and fearless Little My, timid Sniff and the loyal Snorkmaiden. The characters have many adventures on land and in water, and encounter much danger – but always return safely to the Moominhouse. The books are also full of philosophical ideas conveyed with a deceptive simplicity.

Tove created her first Moomin book as a reaction to the traumas of the war years. *The Moomins and the Great Flood*, published in Swedish in 1945, was about Moomintroll and Moominmamma's search for the missing Moominpappa. It was followed by *Comet in Moominland*, but it was not until the publication of the third title, *Finn Family Moomintroll*, that the Moomins began to achieve widespread success. A total of twelve books, which have been translated into over fifty languages, appeared between 1945 and 1977.

In 1952, Associated Newspapers commissioned a Moomin comic strip for London's *Evening News* – the world's largest newspaper. The strip reached up to twenty million readers each day and went on to feature in newspapers all over the world. In 1960 it was taken over by Tove's brother Lars and ran until 1975.

As the Moomins' fame grew, they began to appear in television series, plays, films and radio programmes. They inspired an opera and a series of songs and appeared on Finnish stamps and commemorative coins. Moomin merchandise was soon available and loved across the globe. Even Tarja Halonen, President of Finland, was seen proudly wearing a Moomin watch.

Today there are Moomin shops everywhere from Tokyo to Guadalajara, where you can buy everything from Moomintroll mugs to Hattifattener lamps. There is also a Moomin theme park in Finland where, each summer, thousands of children can visit the Moomin house.